Disney's DINOSAUR

Ladybird

Long ago, a group of dinosaurs lived happily in the Nesting Grounds. But danger was not far away…

A fierce enemy dinosaur – a Carnotaur – charged out of the forest and attacked the dinosaurs.

One mother stood by her nest, protecting her eggs. But when the attacker had gone, so had one of the eggs. It had been stolen by a lizard!

The lizard dropped the egg into a river. And as it floated away, a bird swooped down and took the egg to Lemur Island.

A lemur named Plio found the egg. She watched as it started to crack open. Plio took the baby dinosaur in her arms and cared for him.

The lemurs called the dinosaur Aladar, and he grew into a giant Iguanodon.

Aladar loved his lemur family – Plio, Yar, Suri and Zini. They spent hours playing with him.

One day, Plio called, "Come along, it's time to choose your mate."

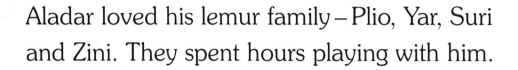

So the young lemurs swung through the trees to choose their mates.

Plio was worried about Aladar. There was no mate on the island for *him*.

Suddenly a huge comet
crashed to Earth! A wave of
fire and water rushed towards
Lemur Island. Aladar
ran across the island,
with Plio, Suri, Yar and Zini
clinging to him.

But the fireball was close
behind! Aladar jumped off a
cliff into the sea, and swam to the mainland.

When they looked back, their home had gone!

The mainland was bare, and a dust cloud rose in the distance. It was a herd of dinosaurs!

"Look at all the Aladars!" cried Suri.

They joined the herd, and became friends with Baylene and Eema, two older dinosaurs. The herd was moving fast and Baylene and Eema couldn't keep up.

"Could you slow down a bit?" Aladar asked their leader.

"No!" growled Kron.

The herd was heading for the Nesting Grounds and Kron wanted to get there quickly. Everyone needed water. And some Carnotaurs were close behind!

When the herd set off again, Aladar saw Neera, Kron's sister – she was beautiful! Plio smiled – maybe Aladar had found a mate after all!

They headed for a lake that Kron said was just over the next hill…

But it wasn't there. The fireball had destroyed it!

The disappointed herd moved on once more, and Aladar helped Eema and Baylene along.

Suddenly Baylene's foot sank into the sand. Water appeared around her foot – they had found water!

As soon as the herd knew this, they stampeded to the water hole. Aladar tried to protect his friends.

Neera liked the way Aladar helped others, and she came to talk to him.

But Kron smelled danger. Carnotaurs! The herd was quickly rounded up, and moved off at great speed.

Baylene and Eema couldn't keep up, so Aladar stayed with them. He watched sadly as the herd disappeared into the distance, Neera with them.

Now the friends were alone. And the Carnotaurs were catching up!

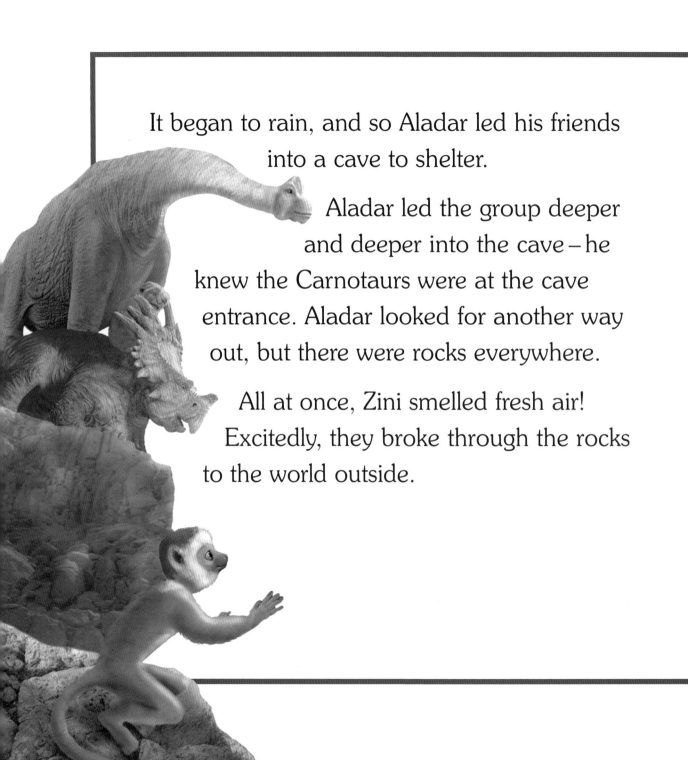

It began to rain, and so Aladar led his friends into a cave to shelter.

Aladar led the group deeper and deeper into the cave – he knew the Carnotaurs were at the cave entrance. Aladar looked for another way out, but there were rocks everywhere.

All at once, Zini smelled fresh air! Excitedly, they broke through the rocks to the world outside.

The friends stepped out of the cave to see the Nesting Grounds before them – with a lake in the middle!

While the others drank and swam, Aladar stared at a pile of rocks caused by a landslide.

"That's the way we used to come here," said Eema.

Aladar thought of Neera. He had to show the herd the new way in.

Aladar went back and found the herd. He told them about the way through the cave, but Kron didn't believe him.

Suddenly, a Carnotaur appeared. He saw Kron, standing alone, and attacked him!

Aladar and Neera went to help but they were too late to save Kron. The dinosaurs then turned to finish their journey.

Some weeks later, in the Nesting Grounds,
Aladar and Neera saw their first baby hatch.

"Oh, happy, happy day!" cheered Eema.
She loved babies.

The old friends all looked down at the
tiny dinosaur and smiled. They were
happy too, safe in their new home.